THINKING IT WAS A WOMAN IN DISTRESS, HARISCHANDRA RUSHED TOWARDS THE SOUND. SOON HE CAME UPON A CLEARING IN THE WOOD.

WHAT HAVE I DONE? THIS IS SAGE VISHWA-MITRA! WHAT CAN I DO NOW?

I AM SORRY I DISTURBED YOU, SIR! I HEARD SOME-ONE CRYING FOR HELP!

IT WAS THE SPIRIT OF SCIENCES I AM TRYING TO MASTER!

I WAS ABOUT TO SUCCEED! YOU HAVE SPOILED EVERYTHING BY COMING HERE! MY CURSE WILL DESTROY YOUR KINGDOM!

IN VAIN DID HARISCHANDRA PLEAD WITH THE SAGE.

ASK FOR ANYTHING AND I SHALL GIVE IT TO YOU!

ANYTHING?

ALL RIGHT! I SHALL REMEMBER YOUR PROMISE!

A FEW DAYS LATER, HARISCHANDRA WAS SEATED ON HIS THRONE. SUDDENLY A LOUD VOICE BROKE THE SILENCE.

HARISCHANDRA!

AS VISHWAMITRA APPROACHED HIM, THE KING FELT UNEASY.

I HAVE COME FOR WHAT YOU PROMISED ME! I WANT YOUR KINGDOM!

MY KINGDOM?

YES! IF YOU FAIL TO KEEP YOUR PROMISE, MY CURSE WILL COME UPON AYODHYA!

AS THE HUSHED COURTIERS WATCHED, HARISCHANDRA TOOK THE SAGE INSIDE.

I HAND OVER MY KINGDOM TO YOU.

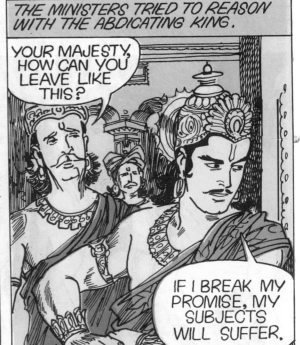

THE MINISTERS TRIED TO REASON WITH THE ABDICATING KING.

YOUR MAJESTY, HOW CAN YOU LEAVE LIKE THIS?

IF I BREAK MY PROMISE, MY SUBJECTS WILL SUFFER.

THE WHOLE CITY CAME TO THE ROAD TO WATCH THE THREE LONELY PEOPLE, HARISCHANDRA, QUEEN SAIVYA AND PRINCE ROHITASWA, GOING AWAY. THEY ALL WEPT, FOR THEY LOVED THEIR KING, THEIR QUEEN AND THE YOUNG PRINCE.

AFTER WALKING A FEW MILES, HARISCHANDRA HEARD SOMEONE CALL HIM FROM BEHIND. HE TURNED ROUND TO FIND THE SAGE VISHWAMITRA COMING TOWARDS THEM.

WAIT!

WITH EVERY GIFT GIVEN, ONE HAD TO GIVE A DAKSHINA— AN HONORARI- UM! HARISCHANDRA HAD GIVEN AWAY EVERYTHING! HE HAD NOTHING LEFT FOR DAKSHINA!

YOU MUST FULFIL YOUR PROMISE! YOUR DAKSHINA IS DUE!

PLEASE GIVE ME A MONTH!

HAVEN'T YOU FORGOTTEN SOMETHING? YOU HAVE MADE A GIFT, BUT WHERE IS THE DAKSHINA?

ONE MONTH IS NEARLY OVER! I HAVE NOT BEEN ABLE TO GET ANY WORK. HOW SHALL I PAY THE SAGE?

HOW LONG SHALL WE ROAM LIKE THIS? THE CHILD IS TIRED.

FATHER! WHY DIDN'T YOU BRING OUR CHARIOT?

AT LAST THEY REACHED THE TEMPLE CITY OF VARANASI.

I HOPE I SHALL GET SOME WORK HERE!

THE TEMPLES OF VARANASI STOOD MAJESTICALLY ON THE BANKS OF THE RIVER GANGA. THE TIRED KING AND HIS FAMILY WENT UP TO A TEMPLE.

DO YOU THINK WE CAN FIND SHELTER HERE?

LET US GO AND MEET THE HIGH PRIEST!

WHO ARE YOU? YOUR FACE SHOWS MARKS OF NOBILITY!

WE ARE WEARY TRAVELLERS! CAN YOU GIVE ME SOME WORK?

WHAT WORK CAN A KSHATRIYA DO IN A TEMPLE? NO, THERE IS NO WORK! BUT TAKE WHATEVER FOOD YOU NEED.

ONE DAY AS THE TRIO WALKED THROUGH THE CROWDED STREET, HARISCHANDRA HEARD A A FAMILIAR VOICE.

HARISCHANDRA!

ONE MONTH IS OVER TODAY!

I KNOW, BUT...

IN A FEW HOURS THE SUN WILL SET! HOW SHALL I PAY THE DAKSHINA?

...THE DAY IS NOT YET OVER! PLEASE WAIT TILL NIGHTFALL.

ROHITASWA, THE YOUNG PRINCE, WAS A BRAVE BOY! HE HAD BORNE THE HARDSHIPS OF HIS PARENTS' EXILE WITH A SMILING FACE. BUT HIS YOUNG BODY COULD NOT BEAR THE STRAIN FOR LONG.

MOTHER! I AM VERY HUNGRY! PLEASE GIVE ME SOME FOOD!

YES, DEAR! YOUR FATHER HAS GONE TO LOOK FOR WORK! HE WILL BRING SOME FOOD!

A FEW HOURS PASSED. THEN HARISCHANDRA CAME BACK. HE COULD NOT FIND ANY WORK.

TAKE THIS FOOD! I BROUGHT IT FROM THE TEMPLE!

DO WE HAVE TO BEG FOR OUR FOOD NOW?

THERE IS ONLY ONE WAY TO FULFIL MY PROMISE! I CAN SELL MYSELF!

OH, NO! NO!

THE MARKETPLACE.

WHO WILL BUY ME? I CAN DO ANY WORK!

LOOK AT THAT FRAIL MAN! WHAT WORK CAN HE DO?

THE DESPERATE KING BESOUGHT MAN AFTER MAN.

WILL YOU BUY ME?

NO, YOU LOOK WEAK!

I MUST SELL MYSELF! I MUST SELL MYSELF!

STANDING UNDER THE MIDDAY SUN, HARISCHANDRA WAS CONSCIOUS OF ONLY THOSE WORDS BEATING IN HIS HEAD.

PLEASE BUY ME!

NOBODY WILL BUY YOU! BUT SOMEONE MAY BUY YOUR WIFE FOR HOUSEWORK!

QUEEN SAIVYA HAD HEARD WHAT THE PASSER-BY HAD SAID. SHE APPROACHED HER HUSBAND.

NO ONE WILL BUY YOU! BUT YOU HAVE SOMETHING ELSE FOR SALE.

WHAT DO YOU MEAN?

I HAVE GIVEN YOU A SON! MY LIFE IS FULFILLED! SELL ME AND PAY YOUR DEBT!

DO YOU KNOW WHAT YOU ARE SAYING? SELL MY OWN WIFE?

TRUTH IS MORE IMPORTANT THAN HUMAN BEINGS! YOU MUST UPHOLD TRUTH! DO YOU REMEMBER WHAT THE SAGE SAID?

YES, I REMEMBER!

WITH A HEAVY HEART HARISCHANDRA WENT TO THE MARKET PLACE. THEY CLIMBED THE PLATFORM ERECTED FOR AUCTIONS. SOON A CROWD GATHERED.

WHO WILL BUY A WOMAN FOR HOUSE-HOLD WORK? MY WIFE IS FOR SALE!

WHAT KIND OF A MAN ARE YOU TO SELL YOUR WIFE?

I AM NO MAN BUT A HEART-LESS MONSTER! BUT I MUST DO WHAT I MUST DO!

A BRAHMAN OFFERED TO BUY THE QUEEN.

I WILL TAKE HER!

WHAT WORK WILL YOU GIVE HER?

SHE WILL BE MY WIFE'S SERVANT. WHAT IS HER PRICE?

HOW CAN A MAN FIX THE PRICE OF HIS WIFE, THE MOTHER OF HIS SON?

THE BRAHMAN WAS DELIGHTED. HE COULD OFFER ANY PRICE HE LIKED.

THEN TAKE THESE FIVE HUNDRED GOLD COINS AND GIVE UP ALL CLAIM ON HER!

I SHALL NOT TOUCH THIS MONEY WITH MY HANDS!

AS HARISCHANDRA REFUSED TO TOUCH THE BAG OF COINS, THE BRAHMAN TIED IT TO HIS WAIST WITH A STRING.

THE YOUNG PRINCE WAS BEWILDERED TO SEE HIS MOTHER GOING AWAY WITH THE OLD BRAHMAN! HE STARTED RUNNING AFTER HER, CRYING LOUDLY.

MOTHER! MOTHER!

HEARING HER SON'S CRY, THE QUEEN'S HEART WAS FILLED WITH PAIN! SHE COULD NOT GO FARTHER!

MOTHER! WHERE ARE YOU GOING?

COME ALONG! WE ARE GETTING LATE!

PLEASE LET ME TAKE HIM WITH ME! HE CAN'T LIVE WITHOUT ME!

THE BRAHMAN WAS GLAD HE COULD BUY THE CHILD ALSO. HE OFFERED SOME MORE MONEY AS THE PRICE OF YOUNG ROHITASWA.

HERE'S ANOTHER TWO-FIFTY! I SHALL BUY THE BOY AS WELL!

MY SON TOO!

I'VE NOTHING ELSE TO LIVE FOR NOW EXCEPT TO PAY MY DEBT!

I CAN HEAR THE FOOTSTEPS OF THE SAGE! NOW I CAN PAY OFF MY DEBT!

HAVE YOU GOT THE MONEY? THE DAY IS ALMOST OVER!

YES!

HARISCHANDRA UNTIED THE PURSE FROM HIS BELT AND GAVE IT TO THE SAGE.

WHAT IS THIS? THIS IS NOT ENOUGH! YOU HAVE TO PAY ME TWO-FIFTY MORE!

NOT ENOUGH? BUT I'VE NOTHING ELSE LEFT!

GET IT SOMEHOW. I SHALL COME AT NIGHTFALL!

WITH A PAINFUL HEART HARISCHANDRA SAT DOWN ON THE STEPS BESIDE THE RIVER. THE DAY WAS WANING. HE KNEW NO WAY OF RAISING MORE MONEY FOR VISHWAMITRA.

I MUST TRY ONCE MORE!

RETURNING TO THE MARKET-PLACE, HARISCHANDRA STOOD ON THE PLATFORM AGAIN—THIS TIME A LONELY FIGURE.

WHO WILL BUY A MAN AS HIS SLAVE?

THE PEOPLE RECOGNISED HIM. MANY LAUGHED.

YOU SOLD YOUR WIFE! IS YOUR NEED FOR MONEY SO GREAT?

YES!

BUT YOU WILL BE A BURDEN TO THE ONE THAT BUYS YOU!

NO ONE WOULD BUY THE LEAN MAN. A CHANDALA WHO WAS THE KEEPER OF THE CREMATION GROUND WAS WATCHING THE AUCTION.

I AM STRONG! IT'S ONLY THAT I'VE NOT EATEN FOR A FEW DAYS! WHO WILL BUY ME?

I SHALL BUY YOU, IF YOU WISH TO BE BOUGHT!

WHAT WORK DO I HAVE TO DO?

WHATEVER WORK A CHANDALA DOES!

DO I HAVE TO LIVE IN THAT HUT?

YES. YOUR DUTY IS TO WAIT ON CREMATORS AND DEMAND THE CLOTH, RICE AND MONEY. A SIXTH PART GOES TO THE KING, THREE TO ME AND THE REST WILL BE YOURS!

HAVE YOU BROUGHT THE PAYMENT?

YES! WE HAVE!

THE SIGHT OF THE PLACE AND THE FLAMES SOON MADE HIS FACE CHANGE. HIS SKIN HAD SHRIVELLED. FEW COULD RECOGNISE HIM.

HE FELT SAD WHEN HE REMEMBERED HIS WIFE AND SON.

THE DAYS PASSED. THE KING WENT ON DOING HIS WORK. THE FIRE BURNT IN THE CREMATION GROUND. THE HEAT AND SMOKE WOULD MIST HARISCHANDRA'S EYES AND HE DREAMT OF HIS LOST KINGDOM.

HE DREAMT OF THE LITTLE PRINCE ASLEEP ON HIS ROYAL BED. IT ALL SEEMED SO FAR AWAY.

MEANWHILE, THE QUEEN HAD TO WORK DAY AND NIGHT IN THE BRAHMAN'S HOUSEHOLD.

WHY ARE YOU CRYING, MY SON?

THE BRAHMAN BEAT ME! I WAS PLAYING IN HIS ROOM!

HER EYES FILLED WITH TEARS, THE QUEEN CARRIED THE DEAD CHILD BACK TO THE HOUSE AND AWOKE THE BRAHMAN.

MY SON IS DEAD. PLEASE GIVE ME SOME MONEY FOR HIS FUNERAL!

MONEY? ISN'T IT ENOUGH THAT WE FEED YOU?

QUIETLY, WITHOUT ANOTHER WORD, THE QUEEN STARTED WALKING THROUGH THE DESERTED STREET OF THE CITY.

NEAR THE GATE OF THE CREMATION GROUND, THE BEARDED CHANDALA BLOCKED HER WAY.

WHAT DO YOU WANT?

HARISCHANDRA COULD NOT SEE THE WOMAN'S FACE WHICH WAS COVERED BY A VEIL.

HAVE YOU BROUGHT THE RICE AND CASH?

NO!

SUDDENLY HARISCHANDRA'S EYES FELL ON THE DEAD CHILD'S FACE.

WAIT!

THE CHILD'S FACE BEARS THE MARK OF ROYALTY! WHO IS HE?

WHY IS MY HEART BEATING SO FAST?

HE IS INDEED A ROYAL CHILD! HIS FATHER WAS HARISCHANDRA!

WHAT DID YOU SAY?

MY SON! MY SON!

WHY DID YOU CRY OUT! LET ME LOOK AT YOUR FACE... MY HUSBAND!

YES! I'M THAT WRETCHED MAN! BUT YOU WILL HAVE TO BRING THE CLOTH AND RICE!

MY HUSBAND WHO WAS A KING IS NOW A CHANDALA? YOU ARE ASKING THE PAYMENT FOR YOUR SON'S FUNERAL?

I HAVE NO CHOICE! I CANNOT DEPRIVE MY MASTER OF HIS DUES!

BEFORE THE CHANDALA COULD REPLY, HARISCHANDRA SAW A MAGNIFICENT SIGHT. THE DEVAS (HEAVENLY BEINGS) HAD COME DOWN TO SEE HIM.

WHAT DOES THIS MEAN?

THEN INDRA, THE KING OF THE DEVAS, CAME FORWARD.

HARISCHANDRA! WE WERE TESTING YOUR DEVOTION TO TRUTH! YOU HAVE PASSED THE SUPREME TEST.

BUT, MY LORD, DID YOU HAVE TO TEST ME BY TAKING AWAY MY ONLY CHILD?

INDRA SMILED.

SEEING INDRA'S SMILE, THE PUZZLED KING TURNED HIS EYES TO WHERE HIS SON'S BODY LAY. HE SAW A STRANGE SIGHT. ROHITASWA WAS STANDING THERE SMILING.

THEN SOMEONE CALLED HIM SOFTLY.

HARISCHANDRA! MY FRIEND, FORGIVE ME FOR TESTING YOU SO HARSHLY!

SAGE VISHWAMITRA?

I HAVE COME TO TAKE YOU TO YOUR KINGDOM!

BUT HOW CAN I GO? I HAVE SOLD MYSELF TO THE CHANDALA!

NO HARISCHANDRA! YOU ARE A FREE MAN! THE CHANDALA WAS YAMA, THE GOD OF VIRTUE, HIMSELF.

YOU HAVE PROVED YOUR VIRTUE! YOU HAVE EARNED YOUR PLACE IN HEAVEN!

I CANNOT GO TO HEAVEN WITHOUT MY SUBJECTS!

YOUR SUBJECTS WILL GET WHAT THEY DESERVE!

IF SO, THEN LET ME SHARE MY BLESSINGS WITH THEM ON THE EARTH!

YOU ARE TRULY A GREAT KING! YOUR REQUEST WILL BE GRANTED!

WORD HAD REACHED THE KINGDOM THAT THE KING WAS COMING BACK. PEOPLE CAME OUT OF THEIR HOUSES TO WELCOME THEIR KING.

THE STREETS WERE LINED BY PEOPLE. MANY WERE CRYING WITH JOY. THE KING WHOM THEY LOVED SO MUCH WAS COMING BACK.